Table of Contents

S0-BRD-598

Grade 2

Program Overview

Component Features

Each *Real-World Problem Solving* reader offers students the following:

- problem-solving questions that provide opportunities for reinforcing skills from the *Math Connects Student Edition*;
- three levels for differentiated instruction—On-level, Approaching, and Spanish;
- content-area instruction in science or social studies that aligns with National standards.

Using Approaching Texts to Differentiate Instruction

The approaching versions of each story are a resource for struggling readers, English Language Learners (ELLs), and students with mild to moderate disabilities. The language of the main text in each on-level book has been modified to make content-area learning more easily accessible for these student populations. Information in charts, maps, graphs, timelines, and tables is identical between on-level and approaching books to allow for consistent mathematical content.

* Approaching versions of each story are denoted with an orange bar on the cover of each book.

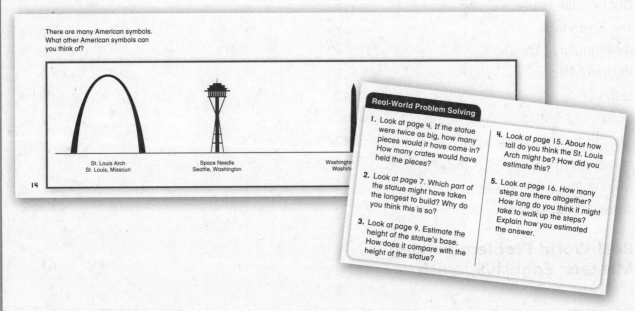

There are many American symbols. What other American symbols can you think of?

St. Louis Arch
St. Louis, Missouri

Space Needle
Seattle, Washington

Washingto
Washin

14

Real-World Problem Solving

1. Look at page 4. If the statue were twice as big, how many pieces would it have come in? How many crates would have held the pieces?

2. Look at page 7. Which part of the statue might have taken the longest to build? Why do you think this is so?

3. Look at page 9. Estimate the height of the statue's base. How does it compare with the height of the statue?

4. Look at page 15. About how tall do you think the St. Louis Arch might be? How did you estimate this?

5. Look at page 16. How many steps are there altogether? How long do you think it might take to walk up the steps? Explain how you estimated the answer.

* On-level titles are available in the classroom Big Book.

Differentiated Instruction:
Approaching and Spanish Titles

Meeting the instructional needs of all learners within the classroom community is a daily challenge for teachers. Organizing instruction of **Real-World Problem Solving** might occur in various ways:

- whole-class instruction with struggling readers, ELLs, and students with mild to moderate disabilities using the approaching texts;

- whole class instruction with struggling readers, ELLs, and students with mild to moderate disabilities grouped using the approaching books. Parallel instructional support may be provided by an instructional aide, intervention specialist, or ELL teacher who monitors and supports understanding;

- small group instruction for struggling readers, ELLs, and students with mild to moderate disabilities;

- each page of teacher support contains a box for approaching level instruction. These tips are intended to activate prior knowledge. As such, they should be used during pre-reading;

- some tips could apply to whole-class instruction, regardless of whether students are reading on-level or approaching texts. These tips might address idiomatic language or other concepts that learners might struggle with. In other cases, the tips address cultural or contextual background building more appropriate for ELL or special education populations.

Real-World Problem Solving Overview

What Makes a Good Problem?

Problem solving and reasoning are processes that students go through as they apply what they know and are able to do when solving a particular problem.

A good math problem:

- engages and appeals to the reader;
- lends itself to a variety of problem-solving solution strategies;
- involves the understanding or use of a math concept or skill;
- has multiple solutions;
- provides opportunities for extension and critical thinking.

The **Real-World Problem Solving** readers are unique in that they feature math problems throughout each story. Each reader ends with a set of 4 to 6 higher-level questions. These questions vary anywhere from a Level 2 question (comprehension) to a Level 4 question (synthesis). (The level of each question is indicated in the annotated pages at the end of the Teacher Guide. Refer to the chart at the bottom of this page to determine what each level means.)

Students are expected to return to the story and find information in the text or in charts, tables, or graphs to answer the questions. Students will solve simple one-step problems all the way up through multi-step, complex problems.

Just as solving problems helps students make sense of the world around them, justifying and explaining their solutions to a particular problem enables them to develop and expand their reasoning skills. **Real-World Problem Solving** readers provide numerous opportunities for the student to read the story and then solve problems, including problems at the higher levels of Bloom's Taxonomy or the Depths of Knowledge.

The Depths of Knowledge include:	
Level 1:	Recall the Basics
Level 2:	Use Basic Concepts and Procedures
Level 3:	Reason and Communicate Understanding
Level 4:	Evaluate, Extend, and Generalize

Communicating Mathematically

It is very important that students communicate mathematically by having them talk or write about the mathematics they are doing. A **Real-World Problem Solving** worksheet master (available in English or Spanish) is provided at the end of the master section. This format guides students through the four-step problem-solving plan and allows them to write the process they used to solve the problem. This is a very important piece of the problem solving process – explaining or justifying the answer to a real-world problem.

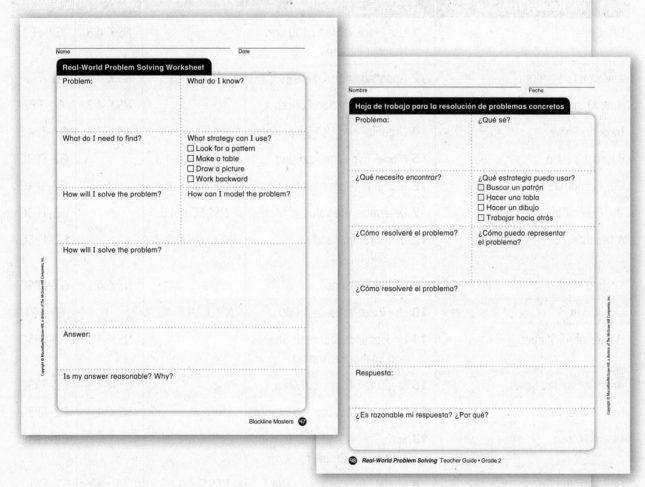

Real-World Problem-Solving Worksheets

Correlations

Real-World Problem Solving Readers
Correlated to National Standards for Mathematics, Social Studies, and Science
Grade 2

CORRELATIONS CHART

Real-World Problem Solving Reader Title	Use With Chapter	Social Studies*	Science*	NCTM**
Life Cycles	**1** Use Place Value to 100 and Number Patterns		NS.K-4.3	G2–FP2
A Magnet's Strength	**2** Apply Addition Concepts		NS.K-4.2	G2–FP2
How Many Seeds?	**3** Apply Subtraction Concepts		NS.K-4.3	G2–FP2
Tracking Snow	**4** Organize and Use Data		NS.K-4.1	G2–FP4C
Baseball's Hero	**5** Model Two-Digit Addition	NSS.USH.K-4.3		G2–FP3C
Our Grandma's Life	**6** Model Two-Digit Subtraction	NSS.USH.K-4.1		G2–FP3C
The Green Cafe	**7** Determine the Value of Money	NSS.EC.K-4.3		G2–FP3C
A Mountain of Presidents	**12** Measure Time and Temperature	NSS.USH.K-4.2		G2–FP5C
Kitchen Math	**9** Model Fractions		NS.K-4.1	G2–FP5C
Lady Liberty	**10** Use Place Value to 1,000	NSS.USH.K-4.2		G2–FP1
Homes of All Shapes	**11** Understand Geometric Shapes and Spatial Reasoning		NS.K-4.3	G2–FP5C
Animals Big and Small	**15** Measure Length and Area		NS.K-4.3	G2–FP5C
Fossils Over Time	**14** Measure Capacity and Weight		NS.K-4.4	G2–FP3C
Moving Along	**13** Solve Three-Digit Addition and Subtraction Problems	NSS.G.K-12.1		G2–FP3C
Geese on the Go	**8** Model Multiplication and Division	NSS.G.K-12.3		G2–FP3C, 6C

* Refer to www.education-world.com for more about the naming conventions used for national social studies and science standards.

*** For a complete correlation to the NCTM Curriculum Focal Points, go to www.macmillanmh.com and select **Math**, then **Teacher View.** The complete Curriculum Focal Points may be viewed at www.nctm.org/focalpoints.*

Life Cycles

NS.K-4.3 Life science

For **Real-World Problem Solving** blackline masters in English and Spanish, see pages 17–18.

Summary

Life Cycles presents the life cycles of butterflies, frogs, mice, and birds. Also included are measurements, charts, and photographs with captions.

Preview and Predict

Review the following vocabulary to activate prior knowledge: *life cycle, stage.*

Ask:

- **How many spots can you find on the wings?**
- **Compare a young animal and its mother. Tell how they are alike and different. Tell how the young animal will grow.**

Read and Respond

Conduct informal assessment of comprehension. Encourage students to apply math skills as they respond to each question. Use prompts such as the following:

- Have students use a ruler to show the wingspan of the largest moth. **Would the smallest moth fit on one of your fingernails?** yes
- **Describe the life cycle of butterfly.** egg, caterpillar, pupa, butterfly
- **A record frog jump is 33 feet, $5\frac{1}{2}$ inches. Could the frog make that jump in this room? How can we find out?** Measure the room and compare the length or width of the room to the frog's jump.
- Have volunteers summarize main points of this story. List responses on the board.

Real-World Problem Solving

- Have students solve the problems using the four-step plan. Then ask them to share which strategy they used to solve.
- Encourage struggling students to work in pairs to solve each problem.
- Ask students to work in pairs or independently to write their own problem. Have them trade problems with one another student and solve.
- Use the worksheet form on pages 47–48.

Real-World Extensions

Ask students to use problem-solving strategies to help them solve problems such as: Three female mice are born in the spring. In the fall, each one of them has 3 female pups. How many female pups did they have? The next spring, each of the female mice has 3 female pups. How many female mice are there all together?

Invite students to find what types of jobs are available that involve animals. Encourage them to investigate how using mathematics plays a role in the jobs that interest them.

Approaching

Reinforce for and/or introduce to students the concepts *pattern* and *repeat*. To demonstrate, create a simple representation of a family tree. Draw stick figure parents on the board. Then draw two or three stick figure children below. Connect the parents to the children. Repeat the same pattern. Explain that a family's life cycle repeats in the same way that the animal life cycles in this book repeat.

Copyright © Macmillan/McGraw-Hill, a division of The McGraw-Hill Companies, Inc.

A Magnet's Strength

NS.K-4.2 Physical science

For **Real-World Problem Solving** blackline masters in English and Spanish, see pages 19–20.

Summary

In *A Magnet's Strength*, students explore a variety of magnets and how we use them in everyday life. The book also presents experiments students can replicate and graphs to analyze and evaluate.

Preview and Predict

Review the following vocabulary to activate prior knowledge: *magnet, strength, magnetic.*
Ask:

- **How do we use magnets in our classroom?** Answers might include to post notes, in computers, on cabinet door latches, in toys.
- **What are some things you can do with a magnet?** Answers will indicate pushing and pulling objects.
- **How does a magnet work?** Answers should indicate that a magnetic field attracts iron or steel.

Read and Respond

Conduct informal assessment of comprehension. Encourage students to apply math skills as they respond to each question. Use prompts such as the following:

- **Look at pages 5 and 6. Which of these objects are magnetic?** paper clips, screws, and pins **Which are not?** cereal, toothpicks, crayons, and buttons
- **Look at pages 11 and 15. Which of the magnets was strongest?** horseshoe magnet **How do you know?** It was able to attract the most objects and at the greatest distance.
- **Will it always be true that a horseshoe magnet is stronger than a bar magnet or**
disk magnet? Why? No, the shape of the magnet does not matter.
- Have volunteers summarize main points of this story. List responses on the board.

Real-World Problem Solving

- Have students solve the problems using the four-step plan. Then ask them to share which strategy they used to solve.
- Encourage struggling students to work in pairs to solve each problem.
- Ask students to work in pairs or independently to write their own problem. Have them trade problems with one another and solve.
- Use the worksheet form on pages 47–48.

Real-World Extensions

 Have students work in teams to find magnetic objects in the classroom. Then have them figure out the most effective ways to display their information. Be sure to tell students to keep magnets away from computers, televisions, microwaves, and pacemakers.

Ask students to use problem-solving strategies to identify what is common about magnetic objects.

Approaching

Using the word *list* as a verb might be unfamiliar to some students. Write a simple list on the board, such as items that students might use to draw a picture (paper, crayons, pencils). Encourage them to contribute ideas. Afterward, tell students you have just written a list. Tell them the same word, *list,* can be used to describe the action of writing the items.

Copyright © Macmillan/McGraw-Hill, a division of The McGraw-Hill Companies, Inc.

How Many Seeds?

NS.K-4.3 Life science

For **Real-World Problem Solving** blackline masters in English and Spanish, see pages 21–22.

Summary
In *How Many Seeds?*, students study a diagram to follow the life cycle of a plant. Students also investigate the numbers of seeds in a variety of plants and read charts to compare and analyze data.

Preview and Predict
Review the following vocabulary to activate prior knowledge: *seed, roots, stems, leaves.*
Ask:

- **What plants do you eat?** Answers might include fruits, vegetables, cereals, and grains.
- **Have you helped with a garden? What grew in the garden?** See students' explanations.
- **Which foods contain seeds?** all plant life

Read and Respond
Conduct informal assessment of comprehension. Encourage students to apply math skills as they respond to each question. Use prompts such as the following:

- **What is the first step in the life cycle of a plant?** the seed **What is the final step?** the fruit **What does the fruit contain?** seeds **If a fruit has 25 seeds, will it grow 25 plants? Why?** It could, but it probably will not because some of the seeds will be eaten and some might not be good.
- **If you make a fruit salad with an apple, an orange, and a kiwi, about how many seeds will you have?** about 110
- Have volunteers summarize main points of this story. List responses on the board.
- Draw a diagram of a plant on the board. Ask students to help you label each part of the plant. Students may turn to page 13 for assistance.

Real-World Problem Solving

- Have students solve the problems using the four-step plan. Then ask them to share which strategy they used to solve.
- Encourage struggling students to work in pairs to solve each problem.
- Ask students to work in pairs or independently to write their own problem. Have them trade problems with one another and solve.
- Use the worksheet form on pages 47–48.

Real-World Extensions

Invite students to count and chart seeds in other fruits and vegetables. Then help students use a computer graphing program to graph the results of their investigations.

Have students use problem-solving strategies to estimate whether there are more seeds in a box of 30 apples or a box of 30 oranges.

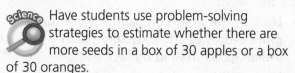

Approaching
Display the photo of the peaches on page 4. Tell students that this fruit has one seed, and point to it. Then display the photo of the kiwi on page 6. Explain that this fruit has many seeds, and point to some of them. Explain to students that different fruits and vegetables have different numbers of seeds.

Copyright © Macmillan/McGraw-Hill, a division of The McGraw-Hill Companies, Inc.

Tracking Snow

NS.K-4.1 Science as inquiry

For **Real-World Problem Solving** blackline masters in English and Spanish, see pages 23–24.

Summary

Tracking Snow presents students with the snowfall of several cities in the United States. Students are asked to use data recorded on graphs and charts to draw conclusions.

Preview and Predict

Review the following vocabulary to activate prior knowledge: *data, average, temperature*.
Ask:

- **What is your favorite kind of weather? Why?** See students' explanations.
- **How can we find out what city gets the most snow?** Check with the weather bureau, Internet, weather channels on television and radio.
- **Look at the cover of *Tracking Snow*. Where in the United States do you think this picture might have been taken?** Sample answers: Chicago; Denver

Read and Respond

Conduct informal assessment of comprehension. Encourage students to apply math skills as they respond to each question. Use prompts such as the following:

- **Look at the graph on page 3. How many more inches of snow usually fall in Indianapolis than in Dallas?** 20 inches
- **Look at the graph on page 11. Which three cities have about the same average snowfall?** Cleveland, Salt Lake City, and Denver
- **What is one important reason Fairbanks, Alaska, gets more snow than Dallas, Texas?** The weather is colder and the cold lasts longer.

- Show students a map of the United States. Point to various cities and ask students to describe why or why not that place may get a lot of snow. Encourage students to use pages in *Tracking Snow* to prove their reasoning.

Real-World Problem Solving

- Have students solve the problems using the four-step plan. Then ask them to share which strategy they used to solve.
- Allow struggling students to work in pairs to solve each problem.
- Ask students to work in pairs or independently to write their own problem. Have them trade problems with one another and solve.
- Use the worksheet form on pages 47–48.

Real-World Extensions

Science Have the students investigate rainfall or snowfall for your area. They can find information on the Internet or from local weather bureaus. Then have the students determine the best way to present their information.

Science Have students work in teams to graph the five greatest snowfalls and the five greatest accumulations in the world in a specified period. Assign each team a different range of years.

Approaching

Explain to students that *tracking* can have different meanings depending on how it is used. For example, on page 5, it is used to mean "record." Then point to the cover photograph. Tell students that this shows how *tracking* can mean "leaving a path," as with footprints.

Copyright © Macmillan/McGraw-Hill, a division of The McGraw-Hill Companies, Inc.

Baseball's Hero

NSS.USH.K-4.3 The history of the United States

For **Real-World Problem Solving** blackline masters in English and Spanish, see pages 25–26.

Summary

In *Baseball's Hero,* students will read about Jackie Robinson's career in Major League Baseball. They will use two-digit addition to answer questions about baseball and Mr. Robinson's accomplishments.

Preview and Predict

Review the following vocabulary to activate prior knowledge: *Major League Baseball, stats, rookie, hits, stolen bases.*

Ask:

- **Have you played baseball or softball? What positions have you played?** See students' explanations.

- **Name some people who are sports heroes.**

- **Who is your hero?** See students' explanations.

Read and Respond

Conduct informal assessment of comprehension. Encourage students to apply math skills as they respond to each question. Use prompts such as the following:

- **Look at the diagram on page 9. What is the distance between bases?** 90 feet **What is the distance all they way around the diamond from home plate back to home plate?** 360 feet

- **How many home runs did Roy Campanella, Pee Wee Reese, and Jackie Robinson hit altogether in 1949?** 54

- Have volunteers summarize main points of this story. List responses on the board.

Real-World Problem Solving

- Have students solve the problems using the four-step plan. Then ask them to share which strategy they used to solve.

- Encourage struggling students to work in pairs to solve each problem.

- Ask students to work in pairs or independently to write their own problem. Have them trade problems with one another and solve.

- Use the worksheet form on pages 47–48.

Real-World Extensions

Encourage students to create their own baseball timeline. Help them find out about the earliest ball-and-bat games, such as European stool ball, rounders, and cricket. Challenge them to write addition problems based on their timelines.

Have small groups of students research different baseball teams. Ask students to choose three players from their team, and students will graph the homeruns of those players. Encourage students to compare their data.

Approaching

Some students may be unfamiliar with the rules and vocabulary specific to baseball. Explain that this game is played between two teams. Each team has nine players. Use the diagram on page 9 to explain how a batter advances based on how far he or she hits the baseball. Explain that a *stolen base* refers to a runner advancing to the next base while the pitcher is throwing a pitch.

Copyright © Macmillan/McGraw-Hill, a division of The McGraw-Hill Companies, Inc.

Our Grandma's Life

NSS.USH.K-4.1 Living and working together in families and communites, now and long ago.

For **Real-World Problem Solving** blackline masters in English and Spanish, see pages 27–28.

Summary

In *Our Grandma's Life,* a young girl talks with her grandmother about the grandmother's life in the early 1960s. They compare life at that time with life now. Students will also use map skills and math skills to understand comparisons and measurements.

Preview and Predict

Review the following vocabulary to activate prior knowledge: *interview, compare.*

Ask:

- **Have you ever talked to an older person about when he or she was a child? How were things different then?**
- **What games did your grandmother or grandfather play as a child?**
- **How do you think the world will be different when you are 60 years old?**

Read and Respond

Conduct informal assessment of comprehension. Encourage students to apply math skills as they respond to each question. Use prompts such as the following:

- **Look at page 6. How many people were in Trini's class after Ana arrived?** 26 **How many are in the little girl's class today?** 19 **What is the difference?** 7
- **Look at page 9. How much would three 41¢ stamps cost?** 123¢, or $1.23
- **Have students discuss cause-and-effect relationships from the selection. For example, they might point out that moving to Florida from Cuba caused Grandma Trini to learn about her surroundings. List responses on the board.**

Real-World Problem Solving

- Have students solve the problems using the four-step plan. Then ask them to share which strategy they used to solve.
- Encourage struggling students to work in pairs to solve each problem.
- Ask students to work in pairs or independently to write their own problem. Have them trade problems with one another and solve.
- Use the worksheet form on pages 47–48.

Real-World Extensions

Have students make a chart that compares prices from the past to current prices. There are many excellent Web sites that provide information about the past. These will be fun and helpful for making comparisons.

Help students compare old road maps to interstate road maps and determine the shortest route between two points.

Approaching

Ask students what they know about their grandparents. Have them explain how their lives are different from their grandparents' experiences as children. Discuss what items might have increased in price since their grandparents were young. Ask them if they can think of anything that might be cheaper now, and to explain why that might be so.

Copyright © Macmillan/McGraw-Hill, a division of The McGraw-Hill Companies, Inc.

The Green Cafe

NSS.EC.K-4.3 Allocation of goods and services

For **Real-World Problem Solving** blackline masters in English and Spanish, see pages 29–30.

Summary
In *The Green Cafe,* students will explore the business of owning a restaurant. They will learn about the expenses and the jobs in a restaurant.

Preview and Predict
Review the following vocabulary to activate prior knowledge: *community, customers, supplies.*
Ask:

- **What is you favorite restaurant? Why do you like to go there?**
- **What is your favorite meal? If you were going to make that meal for dinner, what foods would you need?**
- **How might a restaurant make a neighborhood a nicer place to live?** Answers might indicate that a restaurant provides jobs, a gathering place for people, a good place to eat and have fun.

Read and Respond
Conduct informal assessment of comprehension. Encourage students to apply math skills as they respond to each question. Use prompts such as the following:

- **Look at page 10. Kelly works 4 hours each day. How much does he make a day?** $32 **Mitch works 6 hours. How much does he make?** $48 **What is the difference?** $16
- **Look at page 15. Here is a problem. Jill and Jen go to lunch. Jen gets tomato soup. Jill gets a big green salad. What does their lunch cost?** $7.75
- Ask students to retell the events in the day of Mr. Green. Write their responses on the board as they volunteer answers. Afterward, explain to them that they just listed their responses in a sequence. Ask them how writing the steps involved in the selection are like the steps involved in solving problems in their math textbooks.

Real-World Problem Solving

- Have students solve the problems using the four-step plan. Then ask them to share which strategy they used to solve.
- Encourage struggling students to work in pairs to solve each problem.
- Ask students to work in pairs or independently to write their own problem. Have them trade problems with one another and solve.
- Use the worksheet form on pages 47–48.

Real-World Extensions

There are many excellent Web sites that provide information about businesses and communities. Students can use these sites to familiarize themselves with real-world problem solving exercises.

Ask students to use problem-solving strategies to help them figure out problems such as: How many necklaces does Mika need to sell to make a profit if her total costs are $22 and each necklace sells for $4?

Approaching
Have students think of five items they would put on a menu. Ask them to imagine that they own a restaurant and to explain what they might charge to sell these foods. Explain that as they create a menu, they should consider factors like cost, staffing, and demand.

Copyright © Macmillan/McGraw-Hill, a division of The McGraw-Hill Companies, Inc.

A Mountain of Presidents

NSS.USH.K-4.2 The history of students' own state or region

For **Real-World Problem Solving** blackline masters in English and Spanish, see pages 31–32.

Summary

In *A Mountain of Presidents,* students see the process of carving Mt. Rushmore. In addition to using measuring and mapping skills, they will be able to use photographs to develop an understanding of scale.

Preview and Predict

Review the following vocabulary to activate prior knowledge: *monument, artist, carve.*

Ask:

- **What is Mt. Rushmore?** a monument to four presidents **Have you seen it in person or on television? Tell us about it.**
- **Have you tried to carve something from stone or wood? What did you carve? Was it difficult?**
- **What would you carve into a tall mountain?**

Read and Respond

Conduct informal assessment of comprehension. Encourage students to apply math skills as they respond to each question. Use prompts such as the following:

- **Look at page 2. If you were to travel the perimeter of South Dakota, about how far would you travel?** approximately 1,180 miles
- **Look at page 6. People worked on the monument from October 1927 until October 1941. How many years did people work on Mount Rushmore?** 14 years
- Have volunteers explain the sequence used to build Mt. Rushmore. They might discuss identifying the location, hiring workers, blasting the rock, and carving. List each step on the board. Ask volunteers if there are details that are not provided in the narrative that they might infer would have taken place during the monument's building.

Real-World Problem Solving

- Have students solve the problems using the four-step plan. Then ask them to share which strategy they used to solve.
- Encourage struggling students to work in pairs to solve each problem.
- Ask students to work in pairs or independently to write their own problem. Have them trade problems with one another and solve.
- Use the worksheet form on pages 47–48.

Real-World Extensions

Encourage students to use their problem-solving skills to determine other monument facial dimensions, such as the width of each face on Mt. Rushmore and the sizes of the noses and eyebrows.

Another stunning monument in South Dakota is the Crazy Horse Memorial. Ask the students to explore it and compare its dimensions and history to those of Mt. Rushmore. Educational Web sites will be helpful; monitor students as they conduct research to identify Web sites appropriate to this task.

Approaching

Ask students what other monuments or statues they can think of that are larger than life. Discuss with students what kind of planning is needed for creating this kind of structure. Encourage them to think of ways that using mathematics would be important. Tell them that builders and planners of these structures need to resize an object to the actual size it represents using a *scale*. Display a road map and show the scale as an example.

Copyright © Macmillan/McGraw-Hill, a division of The McGraw-Hill Companies, Inc.

Kitchen Math

NS.K-4.1 Science as inquiry

For **Real-World Problem Solving** blackline masters in English and Spanish, see pages 33–34.

Summary

Kitchen Math provides an opportunity for students to explore cooking and using math in the kitchen. The story presents a simple recipe for making a fruit salad and incorporates opportunities to practice following directions and using fractions.

Preview and Predict

Review the following vocabulary to activate prior knowledge: *recipe, directions, ingredients.*

Ask:

- **Do you help cook? What is your favorite food to cook?**

- **Why do you think we use recipes?** Answers might include so that foods are the same each time we make them, because we might forget how to make a food, so we can give another person instructions.

- **What might the people on the cover be preparing?**

Read and Respond

Conduct informal assessment of comprehension. Encourage students to apply math skills as they respond to each question. Use prompts such as the following:

- **Look at page 2. If you want twice as much dressing, how much yogurt will you use?** 1 cup **How much honey?** 2 tablespoons

- **If 5 people are going to share the salad equally, what fraction of the salad with 2 people eat?** $\frac{2}{5}$ **What fraction will 4 people eat?** $\frac{4}{5}$

- Have volunteers classify and categorize the different recipes introduced in this text.

Real-World Problem Solving

- Have students solve the problems using the four-step plan. Then ask them to share which strategy they used to solve.

- Encourage struggling students to work in pairs to solve each problem.

- Ask students to work in pairs or independently to write their own problem. Have them trade problems with one another and solve.

- Use the worksheet form on pages 47–48.

Real-World Extensions

There are many excellent Web sites that provide information about food safety and cooking with children. Choose recipes for the students to increase or decrease.

After exploring cookbooks and Web sites, invite students to develop their own cookbooks. Help them convert regular recipes to class-size recipes.

Approaching

Ask students if they have ever made a meal before. Have volunteers tell what meals they have helped to prepare. Afterward ask students what ingredients might go into each meal. Tell them that meals often are based on recipes. Explain that this book will show them how to make a meal based on a recipe.

Kitchen Math **9**

Copyright © Macmillan/McGraw-Hill, a division of The McGraw-Hill Companies, Inc.

Lady Liberty

NSS.USH.K-4.2 The history of student's own state or region

For **Real-World Problem Solving** blackline masters in English and Spanish, see pages 35–36.

Summary

In *Lady Liberty,* students explore the Statue of Liberty. They will discover her history and use her dimensions to solve problems. They also will use their mapping skills to explore the area near the statue.

Preview and Predict

Review the following vocabulary to activate prior knowledge: *liberty, statue, symbol.*
Ask:

- **Have you been to New York City? Have you seen the Statue of Liberty? Tell us about her.**
- **Why do you think we have the Statue of Liberty?** Answers might include: to remind us that most families came from other countries, because we are happy to be free.
- **About how tall do you think the statue is?** Encourage students to explain how they estimated to find the answer.

Read and Respond

Conduct informal assessment of comprehension. Encourage students to apply math skills as they respond to each question. Use prompts such as the following:

- **France gave us the statue for our one-hundredth birthday in 1876. How long ago was that?** Depending on the current year, about 130 years ago.
- **Look at pages 14 and 15. Which structure is tallest?** Gateway Arch
- Discuss with students cause-and-effect relationships from the selection. They might cite the effect of shipping the statue in pieces had

on the time it took to build it. List responses on the board.

Real-World Problem Solving

- Have students solve the problems using the four-step plan. Then ask them to share which strategy they used to solve.
- Encourage struggling students to work in pairs to solve each problem.
- Ask students to work in pairs or independently to write their own problem. Have them trade problems with one another and solve.
- Use the worksheet form on pages 47–48.

Real-World Extensions

Let teams of students design board games based on information about the Statue of Liberty. There are many excellent Web sites that provide information about the Statue of Liberty that students can use to learn more.

Encourage teams of students to apply their problem-solving skills to solve this problem. The statue is 305 ft. 6 inches in all. From the top of the torch to the base is 151 ft. 1 inch. How can you determine how tall the base is?

Approaching

Tell students that the word *crate* on page 4 refers to a specific type of box used in shipping. If possible, show a photograph of an old-style shipping crate. Explain that the statue was shipped in pieces in crates similar to this.

Copyright © Macmillan/McGraw-Hill, a division of The McGraw-Hill Companies, Inc.

Homes of All Shapes

NS.K-4.3 Life science

For **Real-World Problem Solving** blackline masters in English and Spanish, see pages 37–38.

Summary

In *Homes of All Shapes,* students explore the variety in homes of people and animals. The book focuses on shapes, sizes, and functions of homes. Diagrams show differences in the sizes and shapes of animal and people homes.

Preview and Predict

Review the following vocabulary to activate prior knowledge: *circle, triangle, square, rectangle, sphere, pyramid, cube, rectangular prism.*
Ask:

- **People live in many different kinds of homes. What kinds of homes have you lived in?**

- **What shape is our classroom? Can you find something in this room that is shaped like a triangle? a circle?**

- **How is this turtle's home like yours? How is it different?** Answers might include both homes protect and provide shelter; the turtle carries its home, but most people don't; the turtle's home is made out of a shell.

Read and Respond

Conduct informal assessment of comprehension. Encourage students to apply math skills as they respond to each question. Use prompts such as the following:

- **Look at page 7. If you put the tents together so that a side face is touching a side face, what shape do you have?** rectangular prism **If you put the tents together so that a door face and a door face are together, what shape do you have?** a triangular prism

- **Look at page 9. What is the shape of the burrow?** cylinder **Why do you think it isn't shaped like a triangular prism?** Answers might include the cylinder shape is easier to dig, it's stronger, it's the shape of the gopher.

- Have volunteers summarize main points of this story. List responses on the board.

Real-World Problem Solving

- Have students solve the problems using the four-step plan. Then ask them to share which strategy they used to solve.

- Encourage struggling students to work in pairs to solve each problem.

- Ask students to work in pairs or independently to write their own problem. Have them trade problems with one another and solve.

- Use the worksheet form on pages 47–48.

Real-World Extensions

Encourage students to explore the variety of animal homes and how animals build them. There are many excellent Web sites that provide information about animal homes that students can use to learn more.

Encourage teams of students to apply their problem-solving skills. How many cells are in the section of bee hive on page 12 of the book? How much bigger is a bald eagle's nest than a robin's nest?

Approaching

Explain to students that the word *story* can mean something other than a tale. Tell them that in this book, *story* means "the space in a building between two levels." Ask them to think of structures in their community that have one, two, and three stories.

Copyright © Macmillan/McGraw-Hill, a division of The McGraw-Hill Companies, Inc.

Animals Big and Small

NS.K-4.3 Life science

For **Real-World Problem Solving** blackline masters in English and Spanish, see pages 39–40.

Summary

In *Animals Big and Small,* students will have opportunities to compare sizes of animals, using nonstandard and standard units. Students will also compare adult animals to their offspring. This book contains a map to show area, charts, and Venn diagrams.

Preview and Predict

Review the following vocabulary to activate prior knowledge: *estimate, centimeter, exhibit.*

Ask:

- **What's the biggest animal you have ever seen in person? What's the smallest?**

- **What is your favorite wild animal?**

- **How are the animals on the cover the same? How are they different?** Answers might include: they are both giraffes; they have similar markings; the adult is much larger and taller than the baby.

Read and Respond

Conduct informal assessment of comprehension. Encourage students to apply math skills as they respond to each question. Use prompts such as the following:

- **Look at pages 4 and 5. If you are visiting the polar bears, about how long will it take you to walk to the elephant exhibit?** about 2 minutes **Estimate how long it would take you to get from the polar bears to the snacks.** about 4 minutes

- **Look at page 12. What is the difference in length between the smallest seahorse and the largest?** about 29 centimeters

- Have volunteers make inferences about other baby animals and their parents based on what

they learned in the selection. Point out the **Did You Know?** on page 9. How many teeth might other adult animals have? Is an animal's size relevant to the number of teeth it has? Record responses on the board.

Real-World Problem Solving

- Have students solve the problems using the four-step plan. Then ask them to share which strategy they used to solve.

- Encourage struggling students to work in pairs to solve each problem.

- Ask students to work in pairs or independently to write their own problem. Have them trade problems with one another and solve.

- Use the worksheet form on pages 47–48.

Real-World Extensions

 Ask students to use problem-solving strategies to help them figure out problems such as: How many seahorses long is an adult elephant's tusk? How many elephant tusks long is an adult polar bear? How many baby polar bears will fit on a desk chair?

 Have students create a marine mural using relative sizes of sea life.

Approaching

Draw a Venn diagram. Using yourself and your mother or father as the other example, list similarities and differences in the appropriate portions of the diagram. Tell the class that animals share traits in common with their parents but are never exactly the same as their parents.

Copyright © Macmillan/McGraw-Hill, a division of The McGraw-Hill Companies, Inc.

Fossils Over Time

NS.K-4.4 Earth and space science

For *Real-World Problem Solving* blackline masters in English and Spanish, see pages 41–42.

Summary

Fossils Over Time answers many questions students have about fossils in general and dinosaurs in particular. Students will have experiences with measurements and tally charts.

Preview and Predict

Review the following vocabulary to activate prior knowledge: *dinosaur, fossil, cavity.*
Ask:

- **Have you collected fossils or seen fossils in a museum? What did you see?**
- **What is your favorite dinosaur?**
- **How can looking at fossils teach us about dinosaurs?**

Read and Respond

Conduct informal assessment of comprehension. Encourage students to apply math skills as they respond to each question. Use prompts such as the following:

- **Look at page 7. What two dinosaurs together were as long as a brachiosaurus?** stegosaurus and triceratops
- **Look at pages 8 and 9. About how many giraffes would be the same height as a brachiosaurus?** about 3
- Have volunteers compare and contrast fossils with dinosaurs. You might draw a Venn diagram to list responses.

Real-World Problem Solving

- Have students solve the problems using the four-step plan. Then ask them to share which strategy they used to solve.
- Encourage struggling students to work in pairs to solve each problem.
- Ask students to work in pairs or independently to write their own problem. Have them trade problems with one another and solve.
- Use the worksheet form on pages 47–48.

Real-World Extensions

Ask students to use problem-solving strategies to help them figure out problems such as: How many children have to lay head-to-toe to be as long as a brachiosaurus, a tyrannosaurus, or another dinosaur? How many microraptors would fit in the bed of a pickup? What is as tall as a brachiosaurus, a tyrannosaurus, or another dinosaur?

 Have students create a dinosaur mural or diorama using relative sizes of plants and animals.

Approaching

Ask students what they know about dinosaurs. Explain that the conclusions scientists draw about dinosaurs are based largely on their fossils. Tell students that fossils are like an animal's skeleton, in that they show us what is left of a living thing from the past. Explain that fossils can be bones, teeth, footprints, tracks, or even nests.

Copyright © Macmillan/McGraw-Hill, a division of The McGraw-Hill Companies, Inc.

Moving Along

NSS.G.K-12.1 The world in spatial terms

For **Real-World Problem Solving** blackline masters in English and Spanish, see pages 43–44.

Summary

In *Moving Along,* students follow the experiences of a family moving from Oklahoma to California in 1950 along US Route 66. The book provides experiences with time and distance and reading maps.

Preview and Predict

Review the following vocabulary to activate prior knowledge: *Route 66, postcard, petroglyph.*
Ask:

- **Have you ever found old picture postcards? What did they show?**
- **Have you taken a long trip by car? Where did you go? What did you see?**
- **Why might people drive across the country?**

Read and Respond

Conduct informal assessment of comprehension. Encourage students to apply math skills as they respond to each question. Use prompts such as the following:

- **Look at pages 4 and 5. Find Flagstaff, Arizona. Is Utah north of south of Flagstaff? How do you know?** It is north. The compass rose shows the directions.
- **Look at page 7. If it is 250 miles from Hydro to Adrian and 198 miles from Hydro to Amarillo, how far is it from Amarillo to Adrian?** 52 miles
- Have volunteers summarize the main ideas in the selection. List summaries on the board.

Real-World Problem Solving

- Have students solve the problems using the four-step plan. Then ask them to share which strategy they used to solve.
- Encourage struggling students to work in pairs to solve each problem.
- Ask students to work in pairs or independently to write their own problem. Have them trade problems with one another and solve.
- Use the worksheet form on pages 47–48.

Real-World Extensions

 Have students investigate temperatures in the Mohave Desert and plot highs and lows for several weeks.

 Have students plan their own trips along Route 66, including mileage from one stop to another.

Approaching

Display pages from the book that show Max's letters to his grandparents. Tell students that people commonly sent postcards during trips to share stories about their travel. Explain that people now use e-mail or blogs to share this kind of information. Ask students to share what they see as the advantages and disadvantages of writing postcards versus sending e-mails or writing blogs.

Copyright © Macmillan/McGraw-Hill, a division of The McGraw-Hill Companies, Inc.

Geese on the Go

NSS.G.K-12.3 Physical systems

For **Real-World Problem Solving** blackline masters in English and Spanish, see pages 45–46.

Summary

Geese on the Go overviews the migration of Canada geese. It includes migration routes, distances, and durations. The book also includes information about Canada geese families.

Preview and Predict

Review the following vocabulary to activate prior knowledge: *migrate, parade, route.*

Ask:

- **Have you seen geese in the wild or in a park? What do you know about them?**
- **Why do you think the giant Canada goose is called a "honker"?** because of the sound it makes
- **Why might Canada geese fly to a different place for part of the year?** They move to be where temperatures are more comfortable and where food is available.

Read and Respond

Conduct informal assessment of comprehension. Encourage students to apply math skills as they respond to each question. Use prompts such as the following:

- **Look at page 11. If there is one goose at the front of the V formation and 8 more on each side, how many are there altogether?** 17
- **Look at page 12. What land animal can reach a speed greater than the flight speed of a Canada goose?** cheetah
- **If a mother goose has 6 babies a year for 5 years, how many babies will she have?** 30
- Have volunteers draw conclusions about other types of migrating animals based on what they

learned in this selection. Students might discuss the patterns of other animals who travel to different climates or how animals know where to migrate.

Real-World Problem Solving

- Have students solve the problems using the four-step plan. Then ask them to share which strategy they used to solve.
- Encourage struggling students to work in pairs to solve each problem.
- Ask students to work in pairs or independently to write their own problem. Have them trade problems with one another and solve.
- Use the worksheet form on pages 47–48.

Real-World Extensions

Social Studies How do birds get from one place to another without maps? Discuss the expression "a bird's-eye view." Then have students try to draw a bird's-eye view of your schoolyard or another familiar place.

Social Studies Ask students to use problem-solving strategies to help them figure out this problem: There are 9 geese flying in V-formation. After leading the formation for a while, the first goose (Goose A) moves to the back for a rest, and one of the next two geese moves forward to lead. After switching the lead 4 times, where will Goose A be? Draw a picture to show your answer.

Approaching

Discuss with students how living things adjust to changes in their environment. For example, people dress according to the weather. Plants bloom or die depending on the weather. Have students look at the map on page 3. Ask them to think about whether people have travel habits similar to Canada geese; that is, do they search for warmer weather when the weather in their hometown becomes cold?

Copyright © Macmillan/McGraw-Hill, a division of The McGraw-Hill Companies, Inc.

Real-World Problem Solving   Life Cycles

1. Is the life cycle of a butterfly a repeating pattern or a growing pattern? Explain your reasoning.

_____

_____

_____

2. Look at page 10. Compare the number of babies that a pet mouse and a field mouse have each year. Which type of mouse has a greater number of babies?

_____

_____

_____

3. Look at page 12. How old are mice when they can care for themselves? How many days old is this? Explain how you solved this problem.

_____

_____

_____

4. Look at the photographs on pages 14 and 15. Create a repeating pattern to show the life cycle of a bird. Describe your pattern to a classmate.

_____

_____

_____

Copyright © Macmillan/McGraw-Hill, a division of The McGraw-Hill Companies, Inc.

Resuelve problemas concretos   Los ciclos de la vida

I. ¿Es el ciclo de vida de una mariposa un patrón repetitivo o uno en crecimiento? Explica tu razonamiento.

_____

_____

_____

2. Observa la página 10. Compara el número de crías que tienen un ratón doméstico y un ratón de campo cada año. ¿Qué tipo de ratón tiene el mayor número de crías?

_____

_____

_____

3. Observa la página 12. ¿Qué edad tienen los ratones cuando se pueden cuidar por sí solos? ¿Cuál es su edad en días? Explica cómo resolviste el problema.

_____

_____

_____

4. Observa las fotografías de las páginas 14 y 15. Crea un patrón repetitivo que muestre el ciclo de vida de un ave. Descríbele tu patrón a un compañero.

_____

_____

_____

Copyright © Macmillan/McGraw-Hill, a division of The McGraw-Hill Companies, Inc.

Name _____

Date _____

Real-World Problem Solving   A Magnet's Strength

1. Look at page 2. Imagine there is the same amount of paper clips on the each side of the magnet. About how many magnets would there be in all?

_____

_____

2. Look at page 6. Estimate how many total objects are shown on the page. How did you find your answer?

_____

_____

3. Look at page 7. How can you tell which magnet might be the strongest?

_____

_____

4. Look at page 10. How many nails did the bar magnet and the disk magnet pick up altogether?

_____

_____

5. Look at the graphs on pages 11 and 15. What is different about the data in each chart? What is the same? How would the data be affected if stronger magnets had been used?

_____

_____

Copyright © Macmillan/McGraw-Hill, a division of The McGraw-Hill Companies, Inc.

Resuelve problemas concretos   La fuerza de un imán

1. Observa la página 2. Imagina que hay la misma cantidad de clips en cada lado del imán. ¿Aproximadamente cuántos imanes hay en total?

_____

_____

2. Observa la página 6. Estima cuántos objetos se muestran en la página. ¿Cómo calculaste la respuesta?

_____

_____

3. Observa la página 7. ¿Cómo puedes saber cuál imán es el más fuerte?

_____

_____

4. Observa la página 10. ¿Cuántos clavos levantaron el imán de barra y el imán de disco juntos?

_____

_____

5. Observa las gráficas en las páginas 11 y 15. ¿Cuál es la diferencia entre los datos de cada tabla? ¿Cuál es la semejanza? ¿Cómo se afectan los datos si se usan imanes más fuertes?

_____

_____

Copyright © Macmillan/McGraw-Hill, a division of The McGraw-Hill Companies, Inc.

Name _____

Date _____

Real-World Problem Solving   How Many Seeds?

1. Look at page 4. If you have 4 peaches, how many seeds do you have?

   _____

   _____

2. Look at page 6. How did you decide whether there are less than or more than 50 seeds?

   _____

   _____

3. Look at page 8. Suppose Ben has 2 apples. He eats both apples. Only seeds are left. About how many seeds does Ben have?

   _____

   _____

4. Look at the photo on page 10. Imagine you want to plant 10 orange trees. Based on the seeds inside of the orange, would you have enough? How do you know?

   _____

   _____

5. Draw a picture of a fruit that has about 5 seeds.

   _____

   _____

6. Look at page 14. Put the fruit in order from most seeds to least seeds.

   _____

   _____

Copyright © Macmillan/McGraw-Hill, a division of The McGraw-Hill Companies, Inc.

Resuelve problemas concretos   ¿Cuántas semillas?

1. Observa la página 4. Si tienes 4 melocotones, ¿cuántas semillas tienes?

_____

2. Observa la página 6. ¿Cómo decidiste si hay menos o más de 50 semillas?

_____

3. Observa la página 8. Supón que Ben tiene 2 manzanas. Se come ambas. Quedan sólo las semillas. ¿Aproximadamente cuántas semillas tiene Ben?

_____

_____

4. Observa la foto en la página 10. Imagina que quieres plantar 10 árboles de naranja. Basándote en las semillas dentro de la naranja, ¿tienes suficientes? ¿Cómo lo sabes?

_____

_____

5. Dibuja una fruta que tenga aproximadamente 5 semillas.

_____

_____

6. Observa la página 14. Coloca las frutas en orden de la que tenga más a menos semillas.

_____

_____

Copyright © Macmillan/McGraw-Hill, a division of The McGraw-Hill Companies, Inc.

Real-World Problem Solving   Tracking Snow

1. Look at page 3. Write a number sentence to show how many more inches of snow falls in Chicago than in Los Angeles.

_____

_____

2. Look at page 3. How many inches of snow falls in Indianapolis each year? How many feet is this?

_____

_____

3. Predict where your community would fit on the bar graph on page 11.

_____

_____

4. Look at page 12. What is the difference between the average temperatures in Fairbanks and Dallas during the month of March? Use the thermometer on page 13 to justify your answer.

_____

_____

5. There are 6 points on a snowflake. Suppose you cut out snowflakes. If you cut 12 points, how many snowflakes will you have made?

_____

_____

Copyright © Macmillan/McGraw-Hill, a division of The McGraw-Hill Companies, Inc.

Resuelve problemas concretos   Datos sobre la nieve

1. Observa la página 3. Escribe una expresión numérica para mostrar cuántas pulgadas más de nieve cayeron en Chicago que en Los Ángeles.

   _____

   _____

2. Observa la página 3. ¿Cuántas pulgadas de nieve caen en Indianápolis cada año? ¿Cuántos pies es eso?

   _____

   _____

3. Haz una predicción de dónde se encontraría tu comunidad en la gráfica de barras de la página 11.

   _____

   _____

4. Observa la página 12. ¿Cuál es la diferencia entre las temperaturas promedio en Fairbanks y Dallas durante el mes de marzo? Usa el termómetro de la página 13 para justificar tu respuesta.

   _____

   _____

5. Hay 6 puntas en un copo de nieve. Supón que recortas copos de nieve. Si cortas 12 puntas, ¿cuántos copos de nieve hiciste?

   _____

   _____

Copyright © Macmillan/McGraw-Hill, a division of The McGraw-Hill Companies, Inc.

Name _____ Date _____

Real-World Problem Solving   Baseball's Hero

1. Look at page 7. How many home runs and stolen bases did Mr. Robinson have?

_____

_____

2. Look at page 9. Suppose you play 1st base shown on the diagram. Which position on the field would be the farthest for you to throw to? Explain your answer.

_____

_____

3. Look at page 11. How many bases did Mr. Robinson steal in 1947 and 1948 altogether?

_____

_____

4. Look at page 11. Which years did Mr. Robinson have the same number of home runs? Tell how you know.

_____

_____

5. Look at page 14. How many more stolen bases did Mr. Robinson have than Pee Wee Reese?

_____

_____

Copyright © Macmillan/McGraw-Hill, a division of The McGraw-Hill Companies, Inc.

Resuelve problemas concretos — El héroe del béisbol

1. Observa la página 7. ¿Cuántos jonrones y bases robadas tuvo el Sr. Robinson?

_____

_____

2. Observa la página 9. Supón que juegas en la 1ra base que se muestra en el diagrama. ¿Cuál sería la posición más lejana en el campo a la que podrías lanzar? Explica tu respuesta.

_____

_____

3. Observa la página 11. ¿Cuántas bases se robó el Sr. Robinson en 1947 y 1948 en total?

_____

_____

4. Observa la página 11. ¿En qué años tuvo el mismo número de jonrones el Sr. Robinson? Indica cómo lo sabes.

_____

_____

5. Observa la página 14. ¿Cuántas bases robadas más que Pee Wee Reese tuvo el Sr. Robinson?

_____

_____

Copyright © Macmillan/McGraw-Hill, a division of The McGraw-Hill Companies, Inc.

Real-World Problem Solving   Our Grandma's Life

1. Look at page 5. Each street name has a number. The numbers are in order. How many streets would you need to cross to get from the gas station at 54th Street to a house on 49th Street? (*Hint:* Find 54 − 49.)

_____

_____

2. Look at page 6. What is the difference between the number of students in your class and the number of students Grandma had in her class?

_____

_____

3. Today if you paid for two stamps with a $1 bill, what would be your change? Use coins to show your work.

_____

_____

4. Look at page 13. Grandma gave the wrong answer. What is the correct answer? Use addition to check your answer.

_____

_____

5. Look at page 15. Sofia walked for 20 seconds after she ran. How many minutes and seconds did Sofia run and walk altogether?

_____

_____

Copyright © Macmillan/McGraw-Hill, a division of The McGraw-Hill Companies, Inc.

Resuelve problemas concretos   La vida de nuestra abuela

1. Observa la página 5. Cada calle tiene un número. Los números están en orden. ¿Cuántas calles necesitarías cruzar para llegar desde la gasolinera en la calle 54 hasta una casa en la calle 49? (*Ayuda:* Calcula 54 – 49.)

_____

_____

2. Observa la página 6. ¿Cuál es la diferencia entre el número de alumnos en tu clase y el número de alumnos que la Abuela tenía en su clase?

_____

_____

3. Si pagan por dos estampillas hay con un billete de $1, ¿cuánto recibirán de cambio? Indica qué operación usaste.

_____

_____

4. Observa la página 13. La abuela dio la respuesta equivocada. ¿Cuál es la respuesta correcta? Usa la suma para verificar tu respuesta.

_____

_____

5. Observa la página 15. Sofía caminó durante 20 segundos después de haber corrido. ¿Cuántos minutos y segundos caminó y corrió Sofía en total?

_____

_____

Copyright © Macmillan/McGraw-Hill, a division of The McGraw-Hill Companies, Inc.

Real-World Problem Solving   The Green Cafe

1. Look at page 7. What is the total cost of Mr. Green's weekly food order? What operation(s) did you use?

_____

_____

2. Look at page 10. A cook at The Green Cafe works for 3 hours. How much will this cook be paid?

_____

_____

3. Look at page 15. You have $8.75. Your lunch costs $6.50. Use coins to show your change.

_____

_____

4. Look at the menu on page 15. Which bills and coins could you use to pay for Mr. Green's Spinach Pie?

_____

_____

5. Janet takes 4 nickels, 8 pennies, 1 quarter, and 2 dimes to the corner store. What is the greatest amount of money that Janet can spend?

_____

_____

Copyright © Macmillan/McGraw-Hill, a division of The McGraw-Hill Companies, Inc.

Resuelve problemas concretos   El café verde

1. Observa la página 7. ¿Cuál es el costo total del pedido semanal de comida del Sr. Green? ¿Qué operación u operaciones usaste?

_____

_____

2. Observa la página 10. Un cocinero en el café del Sr. Green trabaja por 3 horas. ¿Cuánto se la pagará a este cocinero?

_____

_____

3. Observa la página 15. Tu almuerzo costó $6.50. Si ahora tienes $1.75, ¿cuánto dinero tenías al principio?

_____

_____

4. Observa el menú de la página 15. ¿Cuáles billetes y monedas puedes usar para pagar por el pastel de espinacas del Sr. Green?

_____

_____

5. Janet se lleva 4 monedas de 5¢, 8 monedas de 1¢, 1 moneda de 25¢ y 2 monedas de 10¢ a la tienda de la esquina. ¿Cuál es la mayor cantidad de dinero que puede gastar Janet?

_____

_____

Copyright © Macmillan/McGraw-Hill, a division of The McGraw-Hill Companies, Inc.

Real-World Problem Solving   A Mountain of Presidents

1. Look at page 5. How many years did it take to build Mount Rushmore?

   _____

   _____

2. Look at page 13. In the summer, the park opens at 8:00 A.M. In the winter, the park opens 3 hours later. What time does the park open in the winter?

   _____

   _____

3. Look at page 13. How long is the park open each day? How many hours?

   _____

   _____

4. Look at page 14. How much taller is the Eiffel Tower than the Statue of Liberty?

   _____

   _____

5. Look at pages 9 and 14. How much taller is the Washington Monument than the face of Washington on Mount Rushmore?

   _____

   _____

Copyright © Macmillan/McGraw-Hill, a division of The McGraw-Hill Companies, Inc.

Resuelve problemas concretos   Una montaña de presidentes

1. Mira la página 5. ¿Cuántos años tardaron en construir el Monte Rushmore?

_____

_____

2. Mira la página 13. En el verano, el parque abre a las 8 A.M. En el invierno, el parque abre 3 horas después. ¿A qué hora abre el parque en el invierno?

_____

_____

3. Mira la página 13. ¿Cuánto tiempo está abierto el parque cada día? ¿Por cuántas horas?

_____

_____

4. Mira la página 14. ¿Cuánto más alta es la Torre Eiffel que la Estatua de la Libertad?

_____

_____

5. Mira las páginas 9 y 14. ¿Cuánto más alto es el Monumento a Washington que la cara de Washington en el Monte Rushmore?

_____

_____

Copyright © Macmillan/McGraw-Hill, a division of The McGraw-Hill Companies, Inc.

Real-World Problem Solving   Kitchen Math

1. Look at the recipe card on page 2. What could you use to measure 2 cups of melon and 2 cups of berries?

_____

_____

_____

2. Look at the photos on pages 6 and 7. The recipe calls for 2 cups of berries. If you want to use equal parts of strawberries and blueberries, how much would you use of each?

_____

_____

_____

3. Look at the table on page 11. Suppose you want to double your recipe. How will that change the amount of melon and berries you will need? Draw a picture to show the new amounts.

_____

_____

_____

4. Read the question on page 12. Four people do not eat fruit salad. How much **more** will that leave for the four who **do** eat fruit salad?

_____

_____

_____

Copyright © Macmillan/McGraw-Hill, a division of The McGraw-Hill Companies, Inc.

Resuelve problemas concretos   Matemáticas de cocina

1. Observa la tarjeta de la receta de la página 2. ¿Qué puedes usar para medir 2 tazas de melón y 2 tazas de bayas?

_____

_____

_____

2. Observa las fotografías de las páginas 6 y 7. La receta requiere 2 tazas de bayas. Si quieres usar partes iguales de fresas y moras, ¿cuánto usarías de cada una?

_____

_____

_____

3. Observa la tabla de la página 11. Supón que quieres duplicar tu receta. ¿Cómo cambia eso la cantidad de melón y bayas que necesitarás? Haz un dibujo para mostrar las cantidades nuevas.

_____

_____

_____

4. Lee la pregunta de la página 12. Cuatro personas no comen ensalada de frutas. ¿Cuánto **más** dejará eso para las cuatro personas que **sí** comen ensalada de frutas?

_____

_____

_____

Copyright © Macmillan/McGraw-Hill, a division of The McGraw-Hill Companies, Inc.

Real-World Problem Solving Lady Liberty

1. Look at page 4. If the statue were twice as big, how many pieces would it have come in? How many crates would have held the pieces?

   _____

   _____

2. Look at page 7. Which part of the statue might have taken the longest to build? Why do you think this is so?

   _____

   _____

3. Look at page 9. Estimate the height of the statue's base. How does it compare with the height of the statue?

   _____

   _____

4. Look at page 15. About how tall do you think the Gateway Arch might be? How did you estimate this?

   _____

   _____

5. Look at page 16. How many steps are there altogether? How long do you think it might take to walk up the steps? Explain how you estimated the answer.

   _____

   _____

Copyright © Macmillan/McGraw-Hill, a division of The McGraw-Hill Companies, Inc.

Resuelve problemas concretos La dama de la libertad

1. Observa la página 4. Si la estatua fuese el doble de grande, ¿en cuántas piezas hubiese venido? ¿Cuántas cajas hubiesen cargado las piezas?

_____

_____

2. Observa la página 7. ¿Qué parte de la estatua hubiese tomado más tiempo en construir? ¿Por qué crees que es así?

_____

_____

3. Observa la página 9. Estima la altura de la base de la estatua. ¿Cómo se compara con la altura de la estatua?

_____

_____

4. Observa la página 15. ¿Aproximadamente cuánto crees que mide el arco de Gateway? ¿Cómo estimaste esta medida?

_____

_____

5. Observa la página 16. ¿Cuántos escalones hay en total? ¿Cuánto tiempo crees que tomará subir todos los escalones? Explica cómo estimaste la respuesta.

_____

_____

Copyright © Macmillan/McGraw-Hill, a division of The McGraw-Hill Companies, Inc.

Real-World Problem Solving   Homes of All Shapes

1. Look at the photograph on page 2. About how many rectangles do you see?

   _____

   _____

2. Trace one of the houses on page 3. Draw lines to show how you could cut apart this figure to form one square and three triangles.

   _____

   _____

3. Trace one of the hexagons on page 12. Label the sides and vertices.

   _____

   _____

4. Look at the hamster's home on page 14. How many faces does this home have?

   _____

   _____

5. Compare the shape of Earth with a pyramid. Describe how these figures are alike and how they are different.

   _____

   _____

6. Design a doghouse. Use at least one 3-dimensional shape and three 2-dimensional shapes.

   _____

   _____

Copyright © Macmillan/McGraw-Hill, a division of The McGraw-Hill Companies, Inc.

Resuelve problemas concretos   Hogares de todas las formas

1. Observa la fotografía de la página 2. Aproximadamente, ¿cuántos rectángulos ves?

_____

_____

2. Delinea una de las casas de la página 3. Dibuja líneas para mostrar cómo puedes cortar en partes esta figura para formar un cuadrado y tres triángulos.

_____

_____

3. Delinea uno de los hexágonos de la página 12. Rotula los lados y los vértices.

_____

_____

4. Observa el hogar del hámster en la página 14. ¿Cuántas caras tiene esa casa?

_____

_____

5. Compara la forma de la Tierra con una pirámide. Describe en qué se parecen esas figuras y en qué se diferencian.

_____

_____

6. Diseña una casa para perro. Usa por lo menos una forma tridimensional y tres formas bidimensionales.

_____

_____

Copyright © Macmillan/McGraw-Hill, a division of The McGraw-Hill Companies, Inc.

Real-World Problem Solving   Animals Big and Small

I. Look at page 4. Use pattern blocks to estimate the area of the frog section.

_____

_____

2. Look at the table on page 7. Use pattern blocks to model the length of a baby polar bear. How did you know how many pattern blocks to use?

_____

_____

3. Compare the length of a baby polar bear with the length of an adult female. What is the difference in length?

_____

_____

4. In 3 years, how many centimeters do the tusks of an adult elephant grow? Describe two different ways to solve this problem.

_____

_____

5. Draw a picture of a blue poison frog. Make your picture the actual size of the frog. Explain how you could use a pattern block to check your measurement.

_____

_____

Copyright © Macmillan/McGraw-Hill, a division of The McGraw-Hill Companies, Inc.

Resuelve problemas concretos   Animales grandes y pequeños

1. Observa la página 4. Usa bloques de patrones para estimar el área de la sección de las ranas.

_____

_____

2. Observa la tabla de la página 7. Usa bloques de patrones para representar la longitud de un oso polar bebé. ¿Cómo supiste cuántos bloques de patrones usar?

_____

_____

3. Compara la longitud de un oso polar bebé con la longitud de una osa polar adulta. ¿Cuál es la diferencia en las longitudes?

_____

_____

4. ¿Cuántos centímetros crecen los colmillos de un elefante adulto en 3 años? Describe dos maneras diferentes de resolver este problema.

_____

_____

5. Haz un dibujo de una rana azul venenosa. Haz tu dibujo del tamaño real de la rana. Explica cómo puedes usar un bloque de patrones para verificar tu medida.

_____

_____

Copyright © Macmillan/McGraw-Hill, a division of The McGraw-Hill Companies, Inc.

Name _____ Date _____

Real-World Problem Solving   Fossils Over Time

1. Look at page 3. One dinosaur called a Compsognathus weighed about 7 pounds. Explain how to find how much more a Troodon weighed.

_____

_____

_____

2. Look at page 4. How many centimeters taller are you than a Microraptor? How did you find your answer?

_____

_____

_____

3. Use page 7 to find the total length of a Brachiosaurus and a Triceratops. Is that length greater or less than the total length of a Stegosaurus and Tyrannosaurus rex? Explain.

_____

_____

_____

4. Draw a picture to show how many cups of water could fit inside the brain cavity of 3 T. rex dinosaurs.

_____

_____

_____

Copyright © Macmillan/McGraw-Hill, a division of The McGraw-Hill Companies, Inc.

Resuelve problemas concretos   Fósiles con el tiempo

1. Observa la página 3. Un dinosaurio llamado Compsognathus pesaba cerca de 7 libras. Explica cómo calcular cuánto más pesaba un Troodon.

_____

_____

_____

2. Observa la página 4. ¿Cuántos centímetros más mides tú que un Microraptor? ¿Cómo calculaste tu respuesta?

_____

_____

_____

3. Usa la página 7 para calcular la longitud total de un Braquiosaurio y un Triceratops. ¿Es esa longitud más o menos que la longitud total de un Estegosaurio y un Tiranosaurio? Explica.

_____

_____

_____

4. Haz un dibujo para mostrar cuántas tazas de agua pueden caber dentro de la cavidad del cerebro de 3 Tiranosaurios.

_____

_____

_____

Copyright © Macmillan/McGraw-Hill, a division of The McGraw-Hill Companies, Inc.

Real-World Problem Solving   Moving Along

1. Look at pages 3 and 4. About how many miles is it from Chicago to Tulsa, Oklahoma? How did you find the answer?

_____

_____

2. Look at page 6. Find the map key. If you measure a distance of 2 inches, how many miles would that be?

_____

_____

3. Look at page 9. How many miles is it from Hydro, Oklahoma, to Arizona? How do you know?

_____

_____

4. Look at page 14. How many degrees below freezing can it be at night in the Mohave Desert (freezing = 32° Fahrenheit)?

_____

_____

5. Look at page 15. How many inches does it rain in Oklahoma each year? How could you find the number of feet and inches?

_____

_____

Copyright © Macmillan/McGraw-Hill, a division of The McGraw-Hill Companies, Inc.

Resuelve problemas concretos   Sigue avanzando

1. Mira las páginas 3 y 4. Aproximadamente, ¿cuántas millas hay de Chicago a Tulsa, Oklahoma? ¿Cómo calculaste la respuesta?

_____

_____

2. Observa la página 6. Busca la clave del mapa. Si mides una distancia de 2 pulgadas, ¿cuántas millas representaría eso?

_____

_____

3. Mira la página 9. ¿Cuántas millas hay de Hydro, Oklahoma, a Arizona? ¿Cómo lo sabes?

_____

_____

4. Mira la página 14. ¿Cuántos grados bajo el punto de congelación podría ser la temperatura nocturna en el Desierto de Mohave (punto de congelación = 32° Fahrenheit)?

_____

_____

5. Mira la página 15. ¿Cuántas pulgadas de lluvia recibe Oklahoma cada año? ¿Cómo podrías calcular el número de pies y pulgadas?

_____

_____

Copyright © Macmillan/McGraw-Hill, a division of The McGraw-Hill Companies, Inc.

Real-World Problem Solving   Geese on the Go

1. Look at page 4. Two geese eat 16 times a day. One goose eats 8 times. How many times does the other goose eat?

_____

_____

2. Look at page 5. Three goose families walk together. There are 5 in each line. How many geese are there?

_____

_____

3. Look at page 6. Two geese each lay five eggs. How many eggs are there? What did you do to solve this exercise?

_____

_____

4. Look at page 9. A group of geese fly for 4 hours. They fly this long each day for 5 days. How many hours did they fly altogether for the 5 days?

_____

_____

5. Look at page 11. There are 2 groups of 6 geese. How many geese are there? Explain how you know.

_____

_____

Copyright © Macmillan/McGraw-Hill, a division of The McGraw-Hill Companies, Inc.

Resuelve problemas concretos Gansos de paseo

1. Observa la página 4. Dos gansos comen 16 veces al día. Un ganso come 8 veces. ¿Cuántas veces come el otro ganso?

_____

_____

2. Observa la página 5. Tres familias de gansos caminan juntas. Hay 5 en cada línea. ¿Cuántos gansos hay en total?

_____

_____

3. Observa la página 6. Dos gansos ponen cinco huevos cada uno. ¿Cuántos huevos hay en total? ¿Qué hiciste para resolver este ejercicio?

_____

_____

4. Observa la página 9. Un grupo de gansos vuela durante 4 horas. Ellos vuelan ese tiempo cada día por 5 días. ¿Cuántas horas volaron en total durante los 5 días?

_____

_____

5. Observa la página 11. Hay 2 grupos de 6 gansos. ¿Cuántos gansos hay? Explica cómo lo sabes.

_____

_____

Copyright © Macmillan/McGraw-Hill, a division of The McGraw-Hill Companies, Inc.

Real-World Problem Solving Worksheet

Problem:	What do I know?
What do I need to find?	**What strategy can I use?** ☐ Look for a pattern ☐ Make a table ☐ Draw a picture ☐ Work backward
How will I solve the problem?	**How can I model the problem?**

How will I solve the problem?

Answer:

Is my answer reasonable? Why?

Copyright © Macmillan/McGraw-Hill, a division of The McGraw-Hill Companies, Inc.

Hoja de trabajo para la resolución de problemas concretos

Problema:	¿Qué sé?

¿Qué necesito encontrar?	¿Qué estrategia puedo usar? ☐ Buscar un patrón ☐ Hacer una tabla ☐ Hacer un dibujo ☐ Trabajar hacia atrás
¿Cómo resolveré el problema?	¿Cómo puedo representar el problema?

¿Cómo resolveré el problema?

Respuesta:

¿Es razonable mi respuesta? ¿Por qué?

Copyright © Macmillan/McGraw-Hill, a division of The McGraw-Hill Companies, Inc.

Copyright © Macmillan/McGraw-Hill, a division of The McGraw-Hill Companies, Inc.

Real-World Problem Solving   Life Cycles

1. Is the life cycle of a butterfly a repeating pattern or a growing pattern? Explain your reasoning. **DOK3**

Repeating pattern because the life cycle keeps repeating.

2. Look at page 10. Compare the number of babies that a pet mouse and a field mouse have each year. Which type of mouse has a greater number of babies? **DOK2**

pet mouse

3. Look at page 12. How old are mice when they can care for themselves? How many days old is this? Explain how you solved this problem. **DOK3**

4 weeks old; 28 days. There are 7 days in a week and there are

4 weeks (7 × 4 = 28, or 7 + 7 + 7 + 7 = 28)

4. Look at the photographs on pages 14 and 15. Create a repeating pattern to show the life cycle of a bird. Describe your pattern to a classmate. **DOK3**

See students' work.

A1

Blackline Masters Annos

Resuelve problemas concretos   Los ciclos de la vida

1. ¿Es el ciclo de vida de una mariposa un patrón repetitivo o uno en crecimiento? Explica tu razonamiento. **DOK3**

Es un patrón repetitivo porque el ciclo de la vida sigue

repitiéndose.

2. Observa la página 10. Compara el número de crías que tienen un ratón doméstico y un ratón de campo cada año. ¿Qué tipo de ratón tiene el mayor número de crías? **DOK2**

un ratón doméstico

3. Observa la página 12. ¿Qué edad tienen los ratones cuando se pueden cuidar por sí solos? ¿Cuál es su edad en días? Explica cómo resolviste el problema. **DOK3**

4 semanas; 28 días. Una semana tiene 7 días y hay 4 semanas

(7 × 4 = 28, o 7 + 7 + 7 + 7 = 28)

4. Observa las fotografías de las páginas 14 y 15. Crea un patrón repetitivo que muestre el ciclo de vida de un ave. Descríbele tu patrón a un compañero. **DOK3**

Vea el trabajo de los estudiantes.

17   18

DOK1 Depth of Knowledge 1; **DOK2** Depth of Knowledge 2; **DOK3** Depth of Knowledge 3

Real-World Problem Solving   A Magnet's Strength

1. Look at page 2. Imagine there is the same amount of paper clips on the each side of the magnet. About how many magnets would there be in all? **DOK2**

   about 20

2. Look at page 6. Estimate how many total objects are shown on the page. How did you find your answer? **DOK3**

   about 50; I estimated how many were in each box and added them together.

3. Look at page 7. How can you tell which magnet might be the strongest? **DOK2**

   by looking at which one can pick up the most items

4. Look at page 10. How many nails did the bar magnet and the disk magnet pick up altogether? **DOK2**

   52

5. Look at the graphs on pages 11 and 15. What is different about the data in each chart? What is the same? How would the data be affected if stronger magnets had been used? **DOK3**

   On page 11, the graphs show how many of the objects the magnets pulled. On page 15, the graphs show how far each of the objects are pulled; All the graphs show data about the same types of magnets; If stronger magnets had been used, the number of objects picked up and centimeters pulled would be larger.

Resuelve problemas concretos   La fuerza de un imán

1. Observa la página 2. Imagina que hay la misma cantidad de clips en cada lado del imán. ¿Aproximadamente cuántos imanes hay en total? **DOK2**

   cerca de 20

2. Observa la página 6. Estima cuántos objetos se muestran en la página. ¿Cómo calculaste la respuesta? **DOK3**

   cerca de 50; Estimé cuántos había en cada caja y los sumé todos.

3. Observa la página 7. ¿Cómo puedes saber cuál imán es el más fuerte? **DOK2**

   observando cuál puede levantar más objetos

4. Observa la página 10. ¿Cuántos clavos levantaron el imán de barra y el imán de disco juntos? **DOK2**

   52

5. Observa las gráficas en las páginas 11 y 15. ¿Cuál es la diferencia entre los datos de cada tabla? ¿Cuál es la semejanza? ¿Cómo se afectan los datos si se usan imanes más fuertes? **DOK3**

   En la página 11, las gráficas muestran cuántos objetos halaron los imanes. En la página 15, las gráficas muestran hasta qué distancia se halaron los objetos. Todas las gráficas muestran datos sobre los mismos tipos de imanes; Si se hubieran usado imanes más fuertes, el número de objetos levantados y el número de centímetros recorridos serían mayores.

19   20

A2

DOK1 Depth of Knowledge 1; **DOK2** Depth of Knowledge 2; **DOK3** Depth of Knowledge 3

Copyright © Macmillan/McGraw-Hill, a division of The McGraw-Hill Companies, Inc.

Copyright © Macmillan/McGraw-Hill, a division of The McGraw-Hill Companies, Inc.

Real-World Problem Solving   How Many Seeds?

1. Look at page 4. If you have 4 peaches, how many seeds do you have?   **DOK2**

   4

2. Look at page 6. How did you decide whether there are less than or more than 50 seeds?   **DOK3**

   See students' explanations.

3. Look at page 8. Suppose Ben has 2 apples. He eats both apples. Only seeds are left. About how many seeds does Ben have?   **DOK2**

   10

4. Look at the photo on page 10. Imagine you want to plant 10 orange trees. Based on the seeds inside of the orange, would you have enough? How do you know?   **DOK3**

   No; There aren't 10 seeds in the orange shown on page 10.

5. Draw a picture of a fruit that has about 5 seeds.   **DOK2**

   See students' drawings.

6. Look at page 14. Put the fruit in order from most seeds to least seeds.   **DOK2**

   kiwi, pumpkin, orange, apple, peach

Resuelve problemas concretos   ¿Cuántas semillas?

1. Observa la página 4. Si tienes 4 melocotones, ¿cuántas semillas tienes?   **DOK2**

   4

2. Observa la página 6. ¿Cómo decidiste si hay menos o más de 50 semillas?   **DOK3**

   Vea las explicaciones de los estudiantes.

3. Observa la página 8. Supón que Ben tiene 2 manzanas. Se come ambas. Quedan sólo las semillas. ¿Aproximadamente cuántas semillas tiene Ben?   **DOK2**

   10

4. Observa la foto en la página 10. Imagina que quieres plantar 10 árboles de naranja. Basándote en las semillas dentro de la naranja, ¿tienes suficientes? ¿Cómo lo sabes?   **DOK3**

   No; No hay 10 semillas en la naranja que se muestra en la página 10.

5. Dibuja una fruta que tenga aproximadamente 5 semillas.   **DOK2**

   Vea los dibujos de los estudiantes.

6. Observa la página 14. Coloca las frutas en orden de la que tenga más a menos semillas.   **DOK2**

   kiwi, calabaza, naranja, manzana, melocotón

DOK1 Depth of Knowledge 1; **DOK2** Depth of Knowledge 2; **DOK3** Depth of Knowledge 3

1. Look at page 3. Write a number sentence to show how many more inches of snow falls in Chicago than in Los Angeles. **DOK2**

38 − 0 = 38

2. Look at page 3. How many inches of snow falls in Indianapolis each year? How many feet is this? **DOK3**

24 inches; 2 feet

3. Predict where your community would fit on the bar graph on page 11. **DOK2**

See students' work.

4. Look at page 12. What is the difference between the average temperatures in Fairbanks and Dallas during the month of March? Use the thermometer on page 13 to justify your answer. **DOK3**

46 degrees

5. There are 6 points on a snowflake. Suppose you cut out snowflakes. If you cut 12 points, how many snowflakes will you have made? **DOK3**

2

---

1. Observa la página 3. Escribe una expresión numérica para mostrar cuántas pulgadas más de nieve cayeron en Chicago que en Los Ángeles. **DOK2**

38 − 0 = 38

2. Observa la página 3. ¿Cuántas pulgadas de nieve caen en Indianápolis cada año? ¿Cuántos pies es eso? **DOK3**

24 pulgadas; 2 pies

3. Haz una predicción de dónde se encontraría tu comunidad en la gráfica de barras de la página 11. **DOK2**

Vea el trabajo de los estudiantes.

4. Observa la página 12. ¿Cuál es la diferencia entre las temperaturas promedio en Fairbanks y Dallas durante el mes de marzo? Usa el termómetro de la página 13 para justificar tu respuesta. **DOK3**

46 grados

5. Hay 6 puntas en un copo de nieve. Supón que recortas copos de nieve. Si cortas 12 puntas, ¿cuántos copos de nieve hiciste? **DOK3**

2

23 24

DOK1 Depth of Knowledge 1; DOK2 Depth of Knowledge 2; DOK3 Depth of Knowledge 3

Copyright © Macmillan/McGraw-Hill, a division of The McGraw-Hill Companies, Inc.

Copyright © Macmillan/McGraw-Hill, a division of The McGraw-Hill Companies, Inc.

Real-World Problem Solving   Baseball's Hero

1. Look at page 7. How many home runs and stolen bases did Mr. Robinson have? **DOK2**

   41

2. Look at page 9. Suppose you play 1st base shown on the diagram. Which position on the field would be the farthest for you to throw to? Explain your answer. **DOK3**

   3rd base; See students' explanations.

3. Look at page 11. How many bases did Mr. Robinson steal in 1947 and 1948 altogether? **DOK2**

   51

4. Look at page 11. Which years did Mr. Robinson have the same number of home runs? Tell how you know. **DOK3**

   1947 and 1948; The chart says that he hit 12 home runs for both of those years.

5. Look at page 14. How many more stolen bases did Mr. Robinson have than Pee Wee Reese? **DOK2**

   12

Resuelve problemas concretos   El héroe del béisbol

1. Observa la página 7. ¿Cuántos jonrones y bases robadas tuvo el Sr. Robinson? **DOK2**

   41

2. Observa la página 9. Supón que juegas en la 1ra base que se muestra en el diagrama. ¿Cuál sería la posición más lejana en el campo a la que podrías lanzar? Explica tu respuesta. **DOK3**

   3ra base; Vea las explicaciones de los estudiantes.

3. Observa la página 11. ¿Cuántas bases se robó el Sr. Robinson en 1947 y 1948 en total? **DOK2**

   51

4. Observa la página 11. ¿En qué años tuvo el mismo número de jonrones el Sr. Robinson? Indica cómo lo sabes. **DOK3**

   1947 y 1948; La tabla indica que bateó 12 jonrones en esos dos años

5. Observa la página 14. ¿Cuántas bases robadas más que Pee Wee Reese tuvo el Sr. Robinson? **DOK2**

   12

25 26

DOK1 Depth of Knowledge 1; **DOK2** Depth of Knowledge 2; **DOK3** Depth of Knowledge 3

1. Look at page 5. Each street name has a number. The numbers are in order. How many streets would you need to cross to get from the gas station at 54th Street to a house on 49th Street? (*Hint:* Find 54 − 49.) **DOK3**

5

2. Look at page 6. What is the difference between the number of students in your class and the number of students Grandma had in her class? **DOK2**

See students' work.

3. Look at page 9. If you paid for two stamps with a $1 bill, what would be your change? Use coins to show your work. Sample answer: **DOK2**

Answers will vary depending on stamp price. Sample answer:

42¢ + 42¢ = 84¢; 100¢ − 84¢ = 16¢

4. Look at page 13. Grandma gave the wrong answer. What is the correct answer? Use addition to check your answer. **DOK2**

Sample answer: 31; You can use the dominos to help subtract by crossing out the dots.

5. Look at page 15. Sofia walked for 20 seconds after she ran. How many minutes and seconds did Sofia run and walk altogether? **DOK2**

1 minute, 12 seconds

1. Observa la página 5. Cada calle tiene un número. Los números están en orden. ¿Cuántas calles necesitarías cruzar para llegar desde la gasolinera en la calle 54 hasta una casa en la calle 49? (*Ayuda:* Calcula 54 − 49.) **DOK3**

5

2. Observa la página 6. ¿Cuál es la diferencia entre el número de alumnos en tu clase y el número de alumnos que la Abuela tenía en su clase? **DOK2**

Vea el trabajo de los estudiantes.

3. Si pagan por dos estampillas hoy con un billete de $1, ¿cuánto recibirán de cambio? Indica qué operación usaste. **DOK2**

Las respuestas variarían dependiendo delprecio de las estampillas.

Ejemplo de respuesta: 42¢ + 42¢ = 84¢; 100¢ − 84¢ = 16¢

4. Observa la página 13. La abuela dio la respuesta equivocada. ¿Cuál es la respuesta correcta? Usa la suma para verificar tu respuesta. **DOK2**

Ejemplo de respuesta: 31; Puedes usar los dominós para ayudarte a restar al tachar los puntos.

5. Observa la página 15. Sofía caminó durante 20 segundos después de haber corrido. ¿Cuántos minutos y segundos caminó y corrió Sofía en total? **DOK2**

1 minuto, 12 segundos

Blackline Masters Annos

A6

DOK1 Depth of Knowledge 1; **DOK2** Depth of Knowledge 2; **DOK3** Depth of Knowledge 3

Copyright © Macmillan/McGraw-Hill, a division of The McGraw-Hill Companies, Inc.

Copyright © Macmillan/McGraw-Hill, a division of The McGraw-Hill Companies, Inc.

Real-World Problem Solving   The Green Cafe

1. Look at page 7. What is the total cost of Mr. Green's weekly food order? What operation(s) did you use? **DOK2**

   $22; addition

2. Look at page 10. A cook at The Green Cafe works for 3 hours. How much will this cook be paid? **DOK2**

   $24

3. Look at page 15. You have $8.75. Your lunch costs $6.50. Use coins to show your change. **DOK2**

   See students' work—they should demonstrate $2.25 in change

4. Look at the menu on page 15. Which bills and coins could you use to pay for Mr. Green's Spinach Pie? **DOK2**

   Sample answer: a $5 bill, $1 bill, 4 dimes and 1 nickel

5. Janet takes 4 nickels, 8 pennies, 1 quarter, and 2 dimes to the corner store. What is the greatest amount of money that Janet can spend? **DOK3**

   73 cents

A7

Resuelve problemas concretos   El café verde

1. Observa la página 7. ¿Cuál es el costo total del pedido semanal de comida del Sr. Green? ¿Qué operación u operaciones usaste? **DOK2**

   $22; suma

2. Observa la página 10. Un cocinero en el café del Sr. Green trabaja por 3 horas. ¿Cuánto se la pagará a este cocinero? **DOK2**

   $24

3. Observa la página 15. Tu almuerzo costó $6.50. Si ahora tienes $1.75, ¿cuánto dinero tenías al principio? **DOK2**

   Vas el trabajo de los estudiantes—indica $2.25 en cambio.

4. Observa el menú de la página 15. ¿Cuáles billetes y monedas puedes usar para pagar por el pastel de espinacas del Sr. Green? **DOK2**

   Ejemplo de respuesta: un billete de $5, un billete de $1, 4 monedas de 10¢ y 1 moneda de 5¢

5. Janet se lleva 4 monedas de 5¢, 8 monedas de 1¢, 1 moneda de 25¢ y 2 monedas de 10¢ a la tienda de la esquina. ¿Cuál es la mayor cantidad de dinero que puede gastar Janet? **DOK3**

   73 centavos

29   30

DOK1 Depth of Knowledge 1;   **DOK2** Depth of Knowledge 2;   **DOK3** Depth of Knowledge 3

Real-World Problem Solving   A Mountain of Presidents

1. Look at page 5. How many years did it take to build Mount Rushmore? **DOK2**

14 years

2. Look at page 13. In the summer, the park opens at 8:00 A.M. In the winter, the park opens 3 hours later. What time does the park open in the winter? **DOK2**

11 A.M.

3. Look at page 13. How long is the park open each day? How many hours? **DOK3**

from 8 A.M. to 10 P.M.; 14 hours

4. Look at page 14. How much taller is the Eiffel Tower than the Statue of Liberty? **DOK2**

827 feet taller

5. Look at pages 9 and 14. How much taller is the Washington Monument than the face of Washington on Mount Rushmore? **DOK2**

495 feet taller

Resuelve problemas concretos   Una montaña de presidentes

1. Mira la página 5. ¿Cuántos años tardaron en construir el Monte Rushmore? **DOK2**

14 años

2. Mira la página 13. En el verano, el parque abre a las 8 A.M. En el invierno, el parque abre 3 horas después. ¿A qué hora abre el parque en el invierno? **DOK2**

11 A.M.

3. Mira la página 13. ¿Cuánto tiempo está abierto el parque cada día? ¿Por cuántas horas? **DOK3**

de 8 A.M. a 10 P.M.; 14 horas

4. Mira la página 14. ¿Cuánto más alta es la Torre Eiffel que la Estatua de la Libertad? **DOK2**

827 pies más alto

5. Mira las páginas 9 y 14. ¿Cuánto más alto es el Monumento a Washington que la cara de Washington en el Monte Rushmore? **DOK2**

495 pies más alto

A8

DOK1 Depth of Knowledge 1; **DOK2** Depth of Knowledge 2; **DOK3** Depth of Knowledge 3

Copyright © Macmillan/McGraw-Hill, a division of The McGraw-Hill Companies, Inc.

Copyright © Macmillan/McGraw-Hill, a division of The McGraw-Hill Companies, Inc.

Real-World Problem Solving   Kitchen Math

1. Look at the recipe card on page 2. What could you use to measure 2 cups of melon and 2 cups of berries? **DOK2**

   a measuring cup

2. Look at the photos on pages 6 and 7. The recipe calls for 2 cups of berries. If you want to use equal parts of strawberries and blueberries, how much would you use of each? **DOK2**

   1 cup of each

3. Look at the table on page 11. Suppose you want to double your recipe. How will that change the amount of melon and berries you will need? Draw a picture to show the new amounts. **DOK3**

   4 cups of each; See students' drawings.

4. Read the question on page 12. Four people do not eat fruit salad. How much **more** will that leave for the four who **do** eat fruit salad? **DOK3**

   Sample answer: They will have double the amount they would

   have had if all 8 people ate the salad.

Resuelve problemas concretos   Matemáticas de cocina

1. Observa la tarjeta de la receta de la página 2. ¿Qué puedes usar para medir 2 tazas de melón y 2 tazas de bayas? **DOK2**

   una taza de medir

2. Observa las fotografías de las páginas 6 y 7. La receta requiere 2 tazas de bayas. Si quieres usar partes iguales de fresas y moras, ¿cuánto usarías de cada una? **DOK2**

   1 taza de cada una

3. Observa la tabla de la página 11. Supón que quieres duplicar tu receta. ¿Cómo cambia eso la cantidad de melón y bayas que necesitarás? Haz un dibujo para mostrar las cantidades nuevas. **DOK3**

   4 tazas de cada uno; Vea los dibujos de los estudiantes.

4. Lee la pregunta de la página 12. Cuatro personas no comen ensalada de frutas. ¿Cuánto **más** dejará eso para las cuatro personas que **sí** comen ensalada de frutas? **DOK3**

   Ejemplo de respuesta: Hubieran duplicado la cantidad que

   hubieran usado si las 8 personas comieran ensalada.

Real-World Problem Solving   Lady Liberty

1. Look at page 4. If the statue were twice as big, how many pieces would it have come in? How many crates would have held the pieces? **DOK3**

   700 pieces; 428 crates

2. Look at page 7. Which part of the statue might have taken the longest to build? Why do you think this is so? **DOK3**

   Sample answer: The top part because it has so much detail. See

   students' explanations.

3. Look at page 9. Estimate the height of the statue's base. How does it compare with the height of the statue? **DOK3**

   about 150 feet; Sample answer: The base's height is about the

   same size as the statue's height.

4. Look at page 15. About how tall do you think the Gateway Arch might be? How did you estimate this? **DOK3**

   About 600 feet; Sample answer: It looks like it is twice the height

   of the Statue of Liberty.

5. Look at page 16. How many steps are there altogether? How long do you think it might take to walk up the steps? Explain how you estimated the answer. **DOK3**

   546 steps; See students' explanations.

Resuelve problemas concretos   La dama de la libertad

1. Observa la página 4. Si la estatua fuese el doble de grande, ¿en cuántas piezas hubiese venido? ¿Cuántas cajas hubiesen cargado las piezas? **DOK3**

   700 piezas; 428 cajas

2. Observa la página 7. ¿Qué parte de la estatua hubiese tomado más tiempo en construir? ¿Por qué crees que es así? **DOK3**

   Ejemplo de respuesta: La parte de arriba porque tiene muchos

   más detalles. Vea las explicaciones de los estudiantes.

3. Observa la página 9. Estima la altura de la base de la estatua. ¿Cómo se compara con la altura de la estatua? **DOK3**

   cerca de 150 pies; Ejemplo de respuesta: La altura de la base es

   aproximadamente la misma que la altura de la estatua.

4. Observa la página 15. ¿Aproximadamente cuánto crees que mide el arco de Gateway? ¿Cómo estimaste esta medida? **DOK3**

   Cerca de 600 pies; Ejemplo de respuesta: Parece tener el doble de

   la altura de la Estatua de la Libertad.

5. Observa la página 16. ¿Cuántos escalones hay en total? ¿Cuánto tiempo crees que tomará subir todos los escalones? Explica cómo estimaste la respuesta. **DOK3**

   546 escalones; Vea las explicaciones de los estudiantes.

DOK1 Depth of Knowledge 1; **DOK2** Depth of Knowledge 2; **DOK3** Depth of Knowledge 3

Copyright © Macmillan/McGraw-Hill, a division of The McGraw-Hill Companies, Inc.

Copyright © Macmillan/McGraw-Hill, a division of The McGraw-Hill Companies, Inc.

Resuelve problemas concretos — Hogares de todas las formas

1. Observa la fotografía de la página 2. Aproximadamente, ¿cuántos rectángulos ves? **DOK2**

   cerca de 40

2. Delinea una de las casas de la página 3. Dibuja líneas para mostrar cómo puedes cortar en partes esta figura para formar un cuadrado y tres triángulos. **DOK2**

   Vea los dibujos de los estudiantes.

3. Delinea uno de los hexágonos de la página 12. Rotula los lados y los vértices. **DOK2**

   Vea los dibujos de los estudiantes.

4. Observa el hogar del hámster en la página 14. ¿Cuántas caras tiene esa casa? **DOK2**

   6

5. Compara la forma de la Tierra con una pirámide. Describe en qué se parecen esas figuras y en qué se diferencian. **DOK3**

   Ejemplo de respuesta: Ambas son tridimensionales. La Tierra es una esfera, por lo tanto, no tiene lados ni vértices, mientras que la pirámide sí los tiene.

6. Diseña una casa para perro. Usa por lo menos una forma tridimensional y tres formas bidimensionales. **DOK2**

   Vea los diseños de los estudiantes.

37   38

Real-World Problem Solving — Homes of All Shapes

1. Look at the photograph on page 2. About how many rectangles do you see? **DOK2**

   about 40

2. Trace one of the houses on page 3. Draw lines to show how you could cut apart this figure to form one square and three triangles. **DOK2**

   See students' drawings.

3. Trace one of the hexagons on page 12. Label the sides and vertices. **DOK2**

   See students' drawings.

4. Look at the hamster's home on page 14. How many faces does this home have? **DOK2**

   6

5. Compare the shape of Earth with a pyramid. Describe how these figures are alike and how they are different. **DOK3**

   Sample answer: They are both 3 dimensional. Earth is a sphere, so it does not have sides and vertices, but a pyramid does.

6. Design a doghouse. Use at least one 3-dimensional shape and three 2-dimensional shapes. **DOK2**

   See students' designs.

DOK1 Depth of Knowledge 1; **DOK2** Depth of Knowledge 2; **DOK3** Depth of Knowledge 3

A12

Real-World Problem Solving — Animals Big and Small

1. Look at page 4. Use pattern blocks to estimate the area of the frog section. **DOK2**

   See students' work.

2. Look at the table on page 7. Use pattern blocks to model the length of a baby polar bear. How did you know how many pattern blocks to use? **DOK3**

   See students' explanations.

3. Compare the length of a baby polar with the length of a baby elephant. What is the difference in length? **DOK2**

   61 centimeters

4. In 3 years, how many centimeters do the tusks of an adult elephant grow? Describe two different ways to solve this problem. **DOK3**

   45 cm, 15 × 3 or 15 + 15 + 15

5. Draw a picture of a blue poison frog. Make your picture the actual size of the frog. Explain how you could use a pattern block to check your measurement. **DOK3**

   See students' drawings.

Resuelve problemas concretos — Animales grandes y pequeños

1. Observa la página 4. Usa bloques de patrones para estimar el área de la sección de las ranas. **DOK2**

   Vea el trabajo de los estudiantes.

2. Observa la tabla de la página 7. Usa bloques de patrones para representar la longitud de un oso polar bebé. ¿Cómo supiste cuántos bloques de patrones usar? **DOK3**

   Vea las explicaciones de los estudiantes.

3. Compara la longitud de un oso polar bebé con la longitud de un elefante bebé. ¿Cuál es la diferencia en las longitudes? **DOK2**

   61 centímetros

4. ¿Cuántos centímetros crecen los colmillos de un elefante adulto en 3 años? Describe dos maneras diferentes de resolver este problema. **DOK3**

   45 cm, 15 × 3 o 15 + 15 + 15

5. Haz un dibujo de una rana azul venenosa. Haz tu dibujo del tamaño real de la rana. Explica cómo puedes usar un bloque de patrones para verificar tu medida. **DOK3**

   Vea los dibujos de los estudiantes.

39   40

DOK1 Depth of Knowledge 1; **DOK2** Depth of Knowledge 2; **DOK3** Depth of Knowledge 3

Copyright © Macmillan/McGraw-Hill, a division of The McGraw-Hill Companies, Inc.

Copyright © Macmillan/McGraw-Hill, a division of The McGraw-Hill Companies, Inc.

Real-World Problem Solving Fossils Over Time

1. Look at page 3. One dinosaur called a Compsognathus weighed about 7 pounds. Explain how much more a Troodon weighed. **DOK2**

   Subtract 7 from 110.

2. Look at page 4. How many centimeters taller are you than a Microraptor? How did you find your answer? **DOK3**

   See students' answers.

3. Use page 7 to find the total length of a Brachiosaurus and a Triceratops. Is that length greater or less than the total length of a Stegosaurus and Tyrannosaurus rex? Explain. **DOK3**

   105 feet, less because a Stegosaurus and Tyrannosaurus Rex are 95 feet together.

4. Draw a picture to show how many cups of water could fit inside the brain cavity of 3 T. rex dinosaurs. **DOK2**

   Students' drawings should show 12 cups of water.

Resuelve problemas concretos Fósiles con el tiempo

1. Observa la página 3. Un dinosaurio llamado Compsognathus pesaba cerca de 7 libras. Explica cómo calcular cuánto más pesaba un Troodon. **DOK2**

   Restando 7 de 110.

2. Observa la página 4. ¿Cuántos centímetros más mides tú que un Microraptor? ¿Cómo calculaste tu respuesta? **DOK3**

   Vea las respuestas de los estudiantes.

3. Usa la página 7 para calcular la longitud total de un Braquiosaurio y un Triceratops. ¿Es esa longitud más o menos que la longitud total de un Estegosaurio y un Tiranosaurio? Explica. **DOK3**

   105 pies, menos porque un Estegosaurio y un Tiranosaurio miden 95 pies en total.

4. Haz un dibujo para mostrar cuántas tazas de agua pueden caber dentro de la cavidad del cerebro de 3 Tiranosaurios. **DOK2**

   Los dibujos de los estudiantes deben mostrar 12 tazas de agua.

41 42

DOK1 Depth of Knowledge 1; **DOK2** Depth of Knowledge 2; **DOK3** Depth of Knowledge 3

Blackline Masters Annos

Real-World Problem Solving — Moving Along

1. Look at pages 3 and 4. About how many miles is it from Chicago to Tulsa, Oklahoma? How did you find the answer? **about 760; Sample answer: I used a ruler and it was about 4 inches. The scale on the map says that 1 inch is 190 miles, so 4 inches is 760 miles.** (DOK3)

2. Look at page 6. Find the map key. If you measure a distance of 2 inches, how many miles would that be? **about 700;** (DOK2)

3. Look at page 9. How many miles is it from Hydro, Oklahoma, to Arizona? How do you know? **Sample answer: They had driven 500 miles. It is another 160 miles to Arizona. I added to find total distance.** (DOK3)

4. Look at page 14. How many degrees below freezing can it be at night in the Mohave Desert (freezing = 32° Fahrenheit)? **32 – 10 = 12° below freezing** (DOK2)

5. Look at page 15. How many inches does it rain in Oklahoma each year? How could you find the number of feet and inches? **30 inches; 30 ÷ 12 = 2 feet 6 inches** (DOK3)

Resuelve problemas concretos — Sigue avanzando

1. Mira las páginas 3 y 4. Aproximadamente, ¿cuántas millas hay de Chicago a Tulsa, Oklahoma? ¿Cómo calculaste la respuesta? **cerca de 760; Ejemplo de respuesta: Usé una regla y media alrededor de 4 pulgadas. La escala del mapa indica que 1 pulgada equivale a 190 millas, de modo que, 4 pulgadas equivalen a 760.** (DOK3)

2. Observa la página 6. Busca la clave del mapa. Si mides una distancia de 2 pulgadas, ¿cuántas millas representaría eso? **cerca de 700** (DOK2)

3. Mira la página 9. ¿Cuántas millas hay de Hydro, Oklahoma, a Arizona? ¿Cómo lo sabes? **Ejemplo de respuesta: Manejaron 500 millas. Quedan otras 160 millas hasta Arizona. Sumé para obtener la distancia total.** (DOK2)

4. Mira la página 14. ¿Cuántos grados bajo el punto de congelación podría ser la temperatura nocturna en el Desierto de Mohave (punto de congelación = 32° Fahrenheit)? **32 – 10 = 12° por debajo del punto de congelación** (DOK2)

5. Mira la página 15. ¿Cuántas pulgadas de lluvia recibe Oklahoma cada año? ¿Cómo podrías calcular el número de pies y pulgadas? **30 pulgadas; 2 pies 6 pulgadas** (DOK3)

DOK1 Depth of Knowledge 1; DOK2 Depth of Knowledge 2; DOK3 Depth of Knowledge 3

Copyright © Macmillan/McGraw-Hill, a division of The McGraw-Hill Companies, Inc.

Blackline Masters Annos   A14

Copyright © Macmillan/McGraw-Hill, a division of The McGraw-Hill Companies, Inc.

Real-World Problem Solving   Geese on the Go

1. Look at page 4. Two geese eat 16 times a day. One goose eats 8 times. How many times does the other goose eat? **DOK2**

   8 times

2. Look at page 5. Three goose families walk together. There are 5 in each line. How many geese are there? **DOK2**

   15 geese

3. Look at page 6. Two geese each lay five eggs. How many eggs are there? What did you do to solve this exercise? **DOK3**

   10 eggs; 5 + 5 = 10

4. Look at page 9. A group of geese fly for 4 hours. They fly this long each day for 5 days. How many hours did they fly altogether for the 5 days? **DOK2**

   20 hours

5. Look at page 11. There are 2 groups of 6 geese. How many geese are there? Explain how you know. **DOK3**

   12; Sample answer: Two groups times 6 geese in each group is

   12 (2 × 8 = 16).

DOK1 Depth of Knowledge 1; **DOK2** Depth of Knowledge 2; **DOK3** Depth of Knowledge 3

45 46

Resuelve problemas concretos   Gansos de paseo

1. Observa la página 4. Dos gansos comen 16 veces al día. Un ganso come 8 veces. ¿Cuántas veces come el otro ganso? **DOK2**

   8 veces

2. Observa la página 5. Tres familias de gansos caminan juntas. Hay 5 en cada línea. ¿Cuántos gansos hay en total? **DOK2**

   15 gansos

3. Observa la página 6. Dos gansos ponen cinco huevos cada uno. ¿Cuántos huevos hay en total? ¿Qué hiciste para resolver este ejercicio? **DOK3**

   10 huevos; 5 + 5 = 10

4. Observa la página 9. Un grupo de gansos vuela durante 4 horas. Ellos vuelan ese tiempo cada día por 5 días. ¿Cuántas horas volaron en total durante los 5 días? **DOK2**

   20 horas

5. Observa la página 11. Hay 2 grupos de 6 gansos. ¿Cuántos gansos hay? Explica cómo lo sabes. **DOK3**

   12; Ejemplo de respuesta: Dos grupos por 6 gansos en cada grupo

   es 12 (2 × 8 = 16).